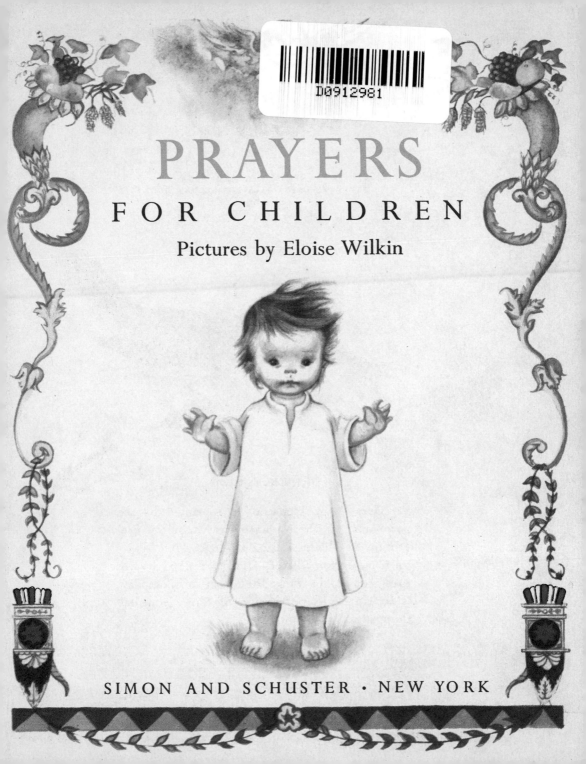

PRAYERS

FOR CHILDREN

Pictures by Eloise Wilkin

SIMON AND SCHUSTER · NEW YORK

THE LITTLE GOLDEN BOOKS ARE PREPARED UNDER THE SUPERVISION OF

MARY REED, Ph.D.

FORMERLY OF TEACHERS COLLEGE, COLUMBIA UNIVERSITY

THIS IS A BRAND-NEW BOOK
ILLUSTRATED ESPECIALLY FOR GOLDEN BOOKS

Acknowledgments

"A Great Gray Elephant" is reprinted by the permission of The National Society for the Prevention of Blindness, Inc., and "A Good Way" by Mary Dixon Thayer, from *The Child on His Knees,* copyright 1928 by The Macmillan Company, is reprinted by permission of The Macmillan Company.

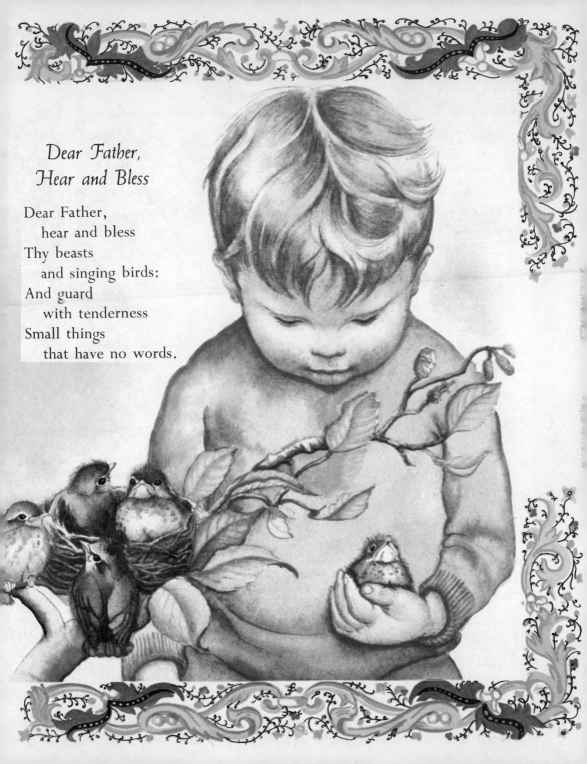

Dear Father,
Hear and Bless

Dear Father,
   hear and bless
Thy beasts
   and singing birds:
And guard
   with tenderness
Small things
   that have no words.

Morning Prayer

Now, before I run to play,
　Let me not forget to pray
To God Who kept me through the night
　And waked me with the morning light.

Help me, Lord, to love Thee more
　Than I ever loved before,
In my work and in my play,
　Be Thou with me through the day.
　　　　　　　　Amen.

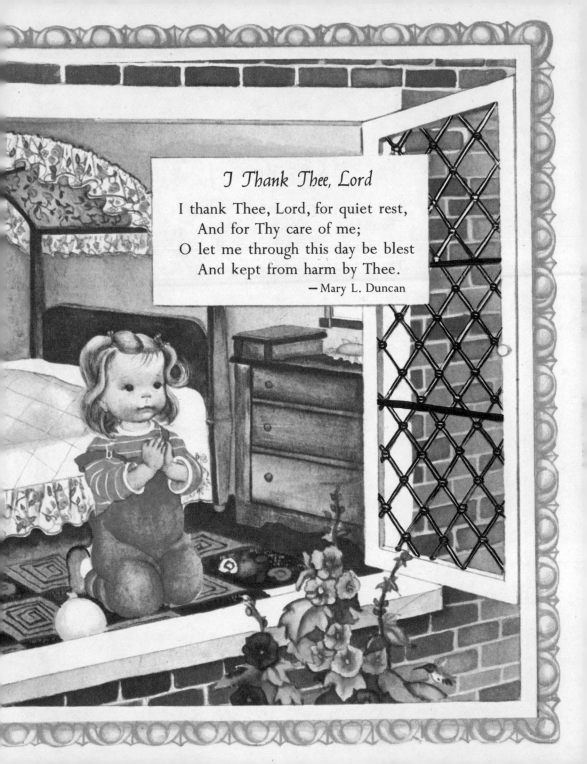

I Thank Thee, Lord

I thank Thee, Lord, for quiet rest,
And for Thy care of me;
O let me through this day be blest
And kept from harm by Thee.

— Mary L. Duncan

A Child's Grace

Thank you for the world so sweet,
Thank you for the food we eat,
Thank you for the birds that sing—
Thank you, God, for everything.
— Mrs. E. R. Leatham

A Child's Grace

God is great and God is good,
And we thank him for our food;
By His hand we must be fed,
Give us, Lord, our daily bread. Amen.

Be present at our table, Lord,
Be here and everywhere adored.
These morsels bless, and grant that we
May feast in Paradise with Thee. Amen.

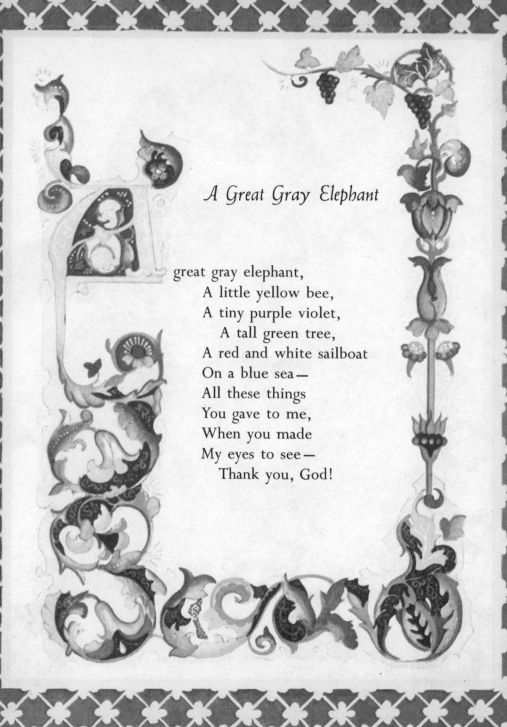

A Great Gray Elephant

A great gray elephant,
   A little yellow bee,
   A tiny purple violet,
      A tall green tree,
   A red and white sailboat
   On a blue sea —
   All these things
   You gave to me,
   When you made
   My eyes to see —
      Thank you, God!

He Prayeth Well,
Who Loveth Well

He prayeth well,
   Who loveth well
Both man and bird and beast.
He prayeth best,
   Who loveth best
All things both great and small;
For the dear God
   Who loveth us,
He made and loveth all.

       —Samuel Taylor Coleridge,
        from *The Ancient Mariner*

Father, We Thank Thee

For flowers that bloom about our feet,
 Father, we thank Thee,
For tender grass so fresh and sweet,
 Father, we thank Thee,
For the song of bird and hum of bee,
For all things fair we hear or see
Father in heaven, we thank Thee.

For blue of stream and blue of sky,
 Father, we thank Thee,
For pleasant shade of branches high,
 Father, we thank Thee,
For fragrant air and cooling breeze,
For beauty of the blooming trees,
Father in heaven, we thank Thee.

For this new morning with its light,
 Father, we thank Thee,
For rest and shelter of the night,
 Father, we thank Thee,
For health and food, for love and friends,
For everything Thy goodness sends,
Father in heaven, we thank Thee.

— Ralph Waldo Emerson

The Lord's Prayer

ur Father, Who art in heaven,
Hallowed be Thy Name.
Thy kingdom come,
Thy will be done,
In earth as it is in heaven.
Give us this day our daily bread,
And forgive us our debts,
As we forgive our debtors.
And lead us not into temptation
But deliver us from evil,
For thine is the kingdom,
And the power, and the glory,
Forever. Amen.

The Doxology

Praise God, from whom all blessings flow;
Praise Him, all creatures here below;
Praise Him above, ye heavenly host:
Praise Father, Son, and Holy Ghost. Amen.

A Child's Prayer

God, make my life a little light,
  Within the world to glow;
A little flame that burneth bright,
  Wherever I may go.

God, make my life a little flower,
  That giveth joy to all,
Content to bloom in native bower,
  Although the place be small.

God, make my life a little song,
  That comforteth the sad,
That helpeth others to be strong,
  And makes the singer glad.

God, make my life a little staff,
  Whereon the weak may rest,
And so what health and strength I have
  May serve my neighbors best.

God, make my life a little hymn
  Of tenderness and praise;
Of faith, that never waxeth dim,
  In all His wondrous ways.
          — M. Betham-Edwards

Jesus, from Thy Throne on High

Jesus, from Thy throne on high,
   Far above the bright blue sky,
Look on me with loving eye;
   Hear me, Holy Jesus.

Be Thou with me every day,
   In my work and in my play,
When I learn and when I pray;
   Hear me, Holy Jesus.

             — Thomas B. Pollock

The Gift

What can I give Him,
 Poor as I am?
If I were shepherd
 I would bring a lamb,
If I were a Wise Man
 I would do my part,—
Yet what can I give Him,
 Give my heart.

— Christina Rossetti

A Good Way

Let's see, dear God, I want to tell
You in a brand new way
"I love you!" But I cannot think
Of anything to say.
I know, dear God! I'll run and do
Something for someone, and
Then when You see me doing it
Of course You'll understand!

— Mary Dixon Thayer

Evening Hymn

I hear no voice, I feel no touch,
  I see no glory bright;
But yet I know that God is near,
  In darkness as in light.

He watches ever by my side,
  And hears my whispered prayer:
The Father for His little child
  Both night and day doth care.
                    — Anonymous

Jesus, Tender Shepherd, Hear Me

Jesus, tender Shepherd, hear me;
  Bless Thy little lamb tonight;
Through the darkness be Thou near me,
  Watch my sleep till morning light.

All this day Thy hand has led me,
  And I thank Thee for Thy care;
Thou has warmed and clothed and fed me;
  Listen to my evening prayer.
                    — Mary L. Duncan

Good-Night Prayer

Father, unto Thee I pray,
Thou hast guarded me all day;
Safe I am while in Thy sight,
Safely let me sleep tonight.

Bless my friends, the whole world bless;
Help me to learn helpfulness;
Keep me ever in Thy sight;
So to all I say good night.

— Henry Johnstone

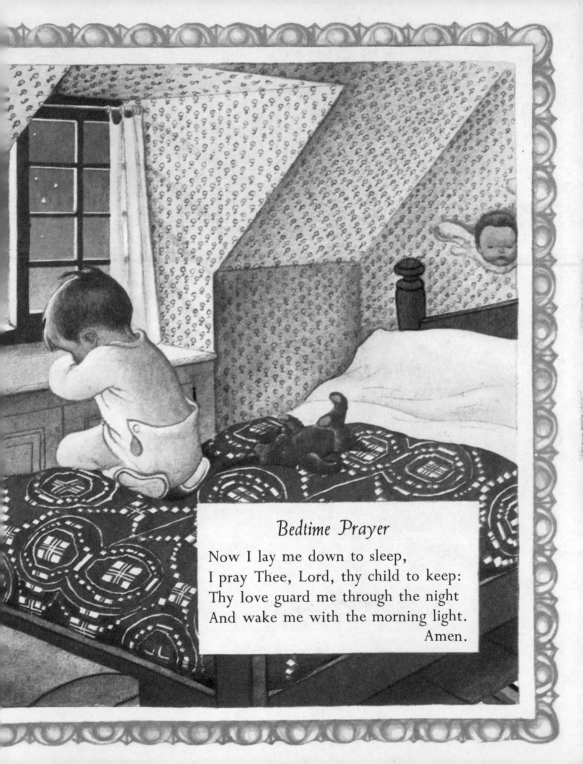

Bedtime Prayer

Now I lay me down to sleep,
I pray Thee, Lord, thy child to keep:
Thy love guard me through the night
And wake me with the morning light.
                                    Amen.

Good Night

Good night! Good night! Far flies the light;
But still God's love shall flame above,
Making all bright. Good night! Good night!

God Watches Us

God watches o'er us all the day, at home, at school, and at our play;
And when the sun has left the skies, he watches with a million eyes.

— Gabriel Setoun

Evening Prayer

Words adapted by Miriam Drury

Miriam Drury

Now I lay me down to sleep, I pray Thee, Lord, Thy child to keep: Thy love guard me through the night, And wake me with the morn-ing light.